M000295106

THE 12 WEEK JOURNAL
FOR MEN'S
Prayer &
Devotional
BIBLE STUDY

written & designed by Shalana Frisby
with Stephen Frisby

More information at: www.123journalit.com

First Printing: February 2017
1 2 3 Journal It Publishing

ISBN-13: 978-1-947209-12-1
Blue Typewriter Cover Edition

TABLE OF CONTENTS

How to use this
JOURNAL

1) Each week **PRAY**, give **THANKS**, read and **STUDY** scripture, **APPLY** it to your life, & **SHARE** it with others.

2) Use the 12 pages per week as a **COMPANION** to your current weekly study time.

3) WRITE, doodle, **DRAW** & ponder your **WEEKLY** Bible study notes to help you better remember **GOD'S WORD**.

...and **ABSOLUTELY** most of all - enjoy your time with the **LORD**...

JOURNAL
property of:

WEEK ONE

dates: _____ to _____

...my study **GOALS** for this week...

This week's **READING** log:

DAY	BOOK	CHAPTER & VERSE

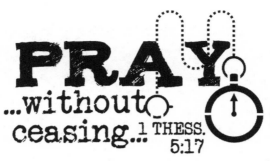

PRAY
...without ceasing... 1 THESS. 5:17

Give God PRAISE first:

_____
_____
_____
_____
_____
_____
_____
_____
_____
_____
_____
_____
_____

Take your cares to the LORD:

_____
_____
_____
_____
_____
_____
_____
_____
_____
_____
_____
_____
_____

...ponder...**WRITE**...doodle...**DRAW**...

Give thanks to
THE LORD
...He is good...
PSALM 136:1

I am
very, very
thankful for...

_____

_____

_____

_____

_____

_____

_____

_____

_____

_____

_____

_____

_____

...ponder... **WRITE**...doodle... **DRAW**...

...additional weekly notes of **THANKS**...

_____

_____

_____

_____

_____

_____

_____

_____

_____

_____

_____

_____

...all scripture is...
GOD-BREATHED
2 TIM. 3:16

Favorite **SCRIPTURES**:

THEMES & KEYWORDS:

...ponder...**WRITE**...doodle...**DRAW**...

...additional weekly **SCRIPTURE** notes...

_____

_____

_____

_____

_____

_____

_____

_____

_____

_____

...my weekly Bible **MEMORY** verse...

_____

_____

_____

_____

_____

_____

How does this week's study APPLY TO MY LIFE?

_____

_____

_____

_____

_____

_____

_____

Who can I SHARE God's word with this week?

This week's **STUDY** notes:

...ponder...**WRITE**...doodle...**DRAW**...

...ponder...**WRITE**...doodle...**DRAW**...

...additional weekly
STUDY notes...

WEEK TWO

dates: _____ to _____

...my study **GOALS** for this week...

This week's **READING** log:

DAY	BOOK	CHAPTER & VERSE

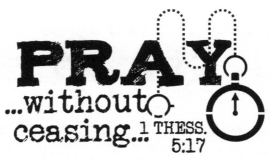

PRAY ...without ceasing... 1 THESS. 5:17

Give God **PRAISE** first:

_____
_____
_____
_____
_____
_____
_____
_____
_____
_____
_____
_____
_____

Take your cares to the **LORD:**

_____
_____
_____
_____
_____
_____
_____
_____
_____
_____
_____
_____
_____

...ponder...**WRITE**...doodle...**DRAW**...

Give thanks to
THE LORD
...He is good...
PSALM 136:1

I am
very, very
thankful for...

...ponder...**WRITE**...doodle...**DRAW**...

...additional weekly notes of **THANKS**...

_____

_____

_____

_____

_____

_____

_____

_____

_____

_____

_____

_____

_____

...all scripture is...
GOD-BREATHED
2 TIM. 3:16

Favorite **SCRIPTURES**:

THEMES & KEYWORDS:

_____

_____

_____

_____

_____

_____

_____

_____

_____

_____

...ponder...**WRITE**...doodle...**DRAW**...

...additional weekly **SCRIPTURE** notes...

_____
_____
_____
_____
_____
_____
_____
_____
_____
_____
_____
_____

...my weekly Bible **MEMORY** verse...

_____
_____
_____
_____
_____
_____

27

How does this week's study APPLY TO MY LIFE?

_____

_____

_____

_____

_____

_____

_____

Who can I **SHARE** God's word with this week?

This week's **STUDY** notes:

...ponder...**WRITE**...doodle...**DRAW**...

...ponder...**WRITE**...doodle...**DRAW**...

...additional weekly
STUDY notes...

WEEK THREE

dates: _____ to _____

...my study **GOALS** for this week...

This week's **READING** log:

DAY	BOOK	CHAPTER & VERSE

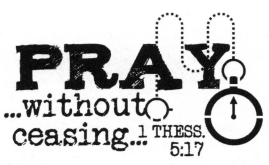

PRAY
...without ceasing... 1 THESS. 5:17

Give God **PRAISE** first:

_____

_____

_____

_____

_____

_____

_____

_____

_____

_____

_____

_____

_____

Take your cares to the **LORD:**

_____

_____

_____

_____

_____

_____

_____

_____

_____

_____

_____

_____

_____

...ponder...**WRITE**...doodle...**DRAW**...

_____

_____

_____

_____

_____

_____

_____

_____

_____

_____

_____

_____

_____

_____

_____

_____

_____

Give thanks to
THE LORD
...He is good...
PSALM 136:1

I am
very, very
thankful for...

_____
_____
_____
_____
_____
_____
_____
_____
_____
_____
_____
_____
_____

...ponder...**WRITE**...doodle...**DRAW**...

...additional weekly notes of **THANKS**...

_____

_____

_____

_____

_____

_____

_____

_____

_____

_____

_____

_____

...all scripture is...
GOD-BREATHED
2 TIM. 3:16

Favorite SCRIPTURES:

THEMES & KEYWORDS:

...ponder...**WRITE**...doodle...**DRAW**...

...additional weekly **SCRIPTURE** notes...

_____
_____
_____
_____
_____
_____
_____
_____
_____
_____
_____

...my weekly Bible **MEMORY** verse...

_____
_____
_____
_____
_____

How does this week's study

APPLY TO MY LIFE?

_____

_____

_____

_____

_____

_____

_____

Who can I SHARE
God's word with this week?

This week's **STUDY** notes:

...ponder...**WRITE**...doodle...**DRAW**...

...ponder...**WRITE**...doodle...**DRAW**...

...additional weekly
STUDY notes...

WEEK FOUR

dates: _____ to _____

...my study **GOALS** for this week...

This week's **READING** log:

DAY	BOOK	CHAPTER & VERSE

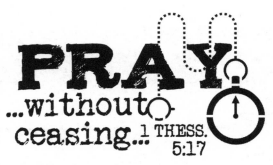

PRAY ...without ceasing... 1 THESS. 5:17

Give God PRAISE first:

_____
_____
_____
_____
_____
_____
_____
_____
_____
_____
_____
_____

Take your cares to the LORD:

_____
_____
_____
_____
_____
_____
_____
_____
_____
_____

...ponder...**WRITE**...doodle...**DRAW**...

...additional weekly **PRAYER** notes...

Give thanks to
THE LORD
...He is good...
PSALM 136:1

I am
very, very
thankful for...

_____

_____

_____

_____

_____

_____

_____

_____

_____

_____

_____

...ponder...**WRITE**...doodle...**DRAW**...

...additional weekly notes of **THANKS**...

...all scripture is...
GOD-BREATHED
2 TIM. 3:16

Favorite **SCRIPTURES**:

_____

_____

_____

_____

_____

_____

_____

_____

_____

_____

THEMES & KEYWORDS:

_____

_____

_____

_____

_____

_____

_____

_____

_____

...ponder...**WRITE**...doodle...**DRAW**...

...additional weekly **SCRIPTURE** notes...

_____

_____

_____

_____

_____

_____

_____

_____

_____

_____

_____

...my weekly Bible **MEMORY** verse...

_____

_____

_____

_____

_____

How does this
week's study
**APPLY TO
MY LIFE?**

_____

_____

_____

_____

_____

_____

_____

Who can I **SHARE**
God's word with this week?

This week's **STUDY** notes:

...ponder...**WRITE**...doodle...**DRAW**...

...additional weekly **STUDY** notes...

WEEK FIVE

dates: _____ to _____

...my study **GOALS** for this week...

This week's **READING** log:

DAY	BOOK	CHAPTER & VERSE

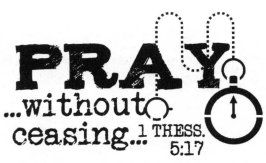

PRAY
...without ceasing... 1 THESS. 5:17

Give God **PRAISE** first:

_____

_____

_____

_____

_____

_____

_____

_____

_____

_____

_____

_____

_____

Take your cares to the **LORD:**

_____

_____

_____

_____

_____

_____

_____

_____

_____

_____

_____

...ponder...**WRITE**...doodle...**DRAW**...

...additional weekly **PRAYER** notes...

Give thanks to
THE LORD
...He is good...
PSALM 136:1

I am
very, very
thankful for...

...ponder... **WRITE**...doodle...**DRAW**...

...additional weekly notes of **THANKS**...

...all scripture is...
GOD-BREATHED
2 TIM. 3:16

Favorite **SCRIPTURES**:

_____
_____
_____
_____
_____
_____
_____
_____
_____
_____

THEMES & KEYWORDS:

_____
_____
_____
_____
_____
_____
_____
_____
_____
_____

...ponder...**WRITE**...doodle...**DRAW**...

...additional weekly **SCRIPTURE** notes...

_____

_____

_____

_____

_____

_____

_____

_____

_____

...my weekly Bible **MEMORY** verse...

_____

_____

_____

_____

_____

_____

How does this week's study APPLY TO MY LIFE?

_____

_____

_____

_____

_____

_____

Who can I SHARE God's word with this week?

This week's **STUDY** notes:

...ponder... **WRITE**...doodle... **DRAW**...

...additional weekly
STUDY notes...

WEEK SIX

dates: _____ to _____

...my study **GOALS** for this week...

This week's **READING** log:

DAY	BOOK	CHAPTER & VERSE

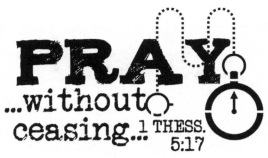

PRAY ...without ceasing... 1 THESS. 5:17

Give God **PRAISE** first:

_____
_____
_____
_____
_____
_____
_____
_____
_____
_____
_____
_____

Take your cares to the **LORD:**

_____
_____
_____
_____
_____
_____
_____
_____
_____
_____
_____
_____

...ponder...**WRITE**...doodle...**DRAW**...

Give thanks to
THE LORD
...He is good...
PSALM 136:1

I am
very, very
thankful for...

_____

_____

_____

_____

_____

_____

_____

_____

_____

_____

_____

_____

_____

...ponder...**WRITE**...doodle...**DRAW**...

...additional weekly notes of **THANKS**...

_____

_____

_____

_____

_____

_____

_____

_____

_____

_____

_____

_____

...all scripture is...
GOD-BREATHED
2 TIM. 3:16

Favorite **SCRIPTURES**:

THEMES & KEYWORDS:

_____

_____

_____

_____

_____

_____

_____

_____

_____

_____

...ponder...**WRITE**...doodle...**DRAW**...

...additional weekly SCRIPTURE notes...

_____

_____

_____

_____

_____

_____

_____

_____

_____

_____

...my weekly Bible MEMORY verse...

_____

_____

_____

_____

_____

How does this week's study APPLY TO MY LIFE?

_____

_____

_____

_____

_____

_____

Who can I SHARE God's word with this week?

This week's **STUDY** notes:

...ponder... **WRITE**...doodle...**DRAW**...

...ponder...**WRITE**...doodle...**DRAW**...

...additional weekly
STUDY notes...

WEEK SEVEN

dates: _____ to _____

...my study **GOALS** for this week...

This week's **READING** log:

DAY	BOOK	CHAPTER & VERSE

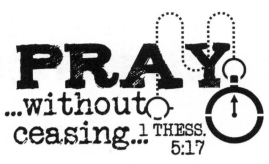

PRAY
...without ceasing... 1 THESS. 5:17

Give God **PRAISE** first:

_____
_____
_____
_____
_____
_____
_____
_____
_____
_____
_____
_____
_____

Take your cares to the **LORD:**

_____
_____
_____
_____
_____
_____
_____
_____
_____
_____
_____
_____
_____

...ponder... **WRITE**...doodle... **DRAW**...

82

Give thanks to
THE LORD
...He is good...
PSALM 136:1

I am
very, very
thankful for...

_____

_____

_____

_____

_____

_____

_____

_____

_____

_____

_____

...ponder... **WRITE**...doodle...**DRAW**...

...additional weekly notes of **THANKS**...

...all scripture is...
GOD-BREATHED
2 TIM. 3:16

Favorite **SCRIPTURES**:

_____

_____

_____

_____

_____

_____

_____

_____

_____

_____

THEMES & KEYWORDS:

_____

_____

_____

_____

_____

_____

_____

_____

_____

_____

...ponder...**WRITE**...doodle...**DRAW**...

...additional weekly **SCRIPTURE** notes...

_____
_____
_____
_____
_____
_____
_____
_____
_____

...my weekly Bible **MEMORY** verse...

_____
_____
_____
_____
_____
_____

How does this week's study **APPLY TO MY LIFE?**

_____

_____

_____

_____

_____

_____

_____

Who can I **SHARE** God's word with this week?

This week's **STUDY** notes:

...ponder... **WRITE**...doodle...**DRAW**...

...additional weekly **STUDY** notes...

WEEK EIGHT

dates: _____ to _____

...my study **GOALS** for this week...

This week's **READING** log:

DAY	BOOK	CHAPTER & VERSE

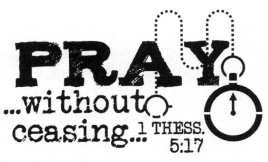

PRAY
...without ceasing... 1 THESS. 5:17

Give God PRAISE first:

_____
_____
_____
_____
_____
_____
_____
_____
_____
_____
_____
_____

Take your cares to the LORD:

_____
_____
_____
_____
_____
_____
_____
_____
_____
_____
_____
_____

...ponder...**WRITE**...doodle...**DRAW**...

...additional weekly **PRAYER** notes...

Give thanks to
THE LORD
...He is good...
PSALM 136:1

I am
very, very
thankful for...

_____

_____

_____

_____

_____

_____

_____

_____

_____

_____

_____

_____

_____

...ponder...**WRITE**...doodle...**DRAW**...

...additional weekly notes of **THANKS**...

...all scripture is...
GOD-BREATHED
2 TIM. 3:16

Favorite **SCRIPTURES**:

THEMES & KEYWORDS:

...ponder...**WRITE**...doodle...**DRAW**...

...additional weekly **SCRIPTURE** notes...

_____

_____

_____

_____

_____

_____

_____

_____

_____

...my weekly Bible **MEMORY** verse...

_____

_____

_____

_____

_____

_____

How does this week's study APPLY TO MY LIFE?

_____

_____

_____

_____

_____

_____

_____

Who can I **SHARE** God's word with this week?

This week's **STUDY** notes:

...ponder...**WRITE**...doodle...**DRAW**...

...ponder...**WRITE**...doodle...**DRAW**...

...additional weekly
STUDY notes...

WEEK NINE

dates: _____ to _____

...my study **GOALS** for this week...

This week's **READING** log:

DAY	BOOK	CHAPTER & VERSE

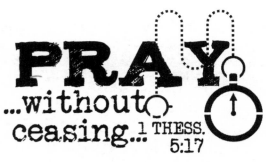

PRAY
...without ceasing... 1 THESS. 5:17

Give God **PRAISE** first:

_____
_____
_____
_____
_____
_____
_____
_____
_____
_____
_____
_____
_____

Take your cares to the **LORD:**

_____
_____
_____
_____
_____
_____
_____
_____
_____
_____
_____
_____
_____

...ponder...**WRITE**...doodle...**DRAW**...

Give thanks to
THE LORD
...He is good...
PSALM 136:1

I am
very, very
thankful for...

_____

_____

_____

_____

_____

_____

_____

_____

_____

_____

_____

...ponder...**WRITE**...doodle...**DRAW**...

...additional weekly notes of **THANKS**...

...all scripture is...
GOD-BREATHED
2 TIM. 3:16

Favorite **SCRIPTURES**:

THEMES & KEYWORDS:

...ponder...**WRITE**...doodle...**DRAW**...

...additional weekly **SCRIPTURE** notes...

_____

_____

_____

_____

_____

_____

_____

_____

_____

_____

...my weekly Bible **MEMORY** verse...

_____

_____

_____

_____

_____

_____

How does this
week's study
**APPLY TO
MY LIFE?**

_____

_____

_____

_____

_____

_____

_____

Who can I **SHARE**
God's word with this week?

This week's **STUDY** notes:

...ponder...**WRITE**...doodle...**DRAW**...

...additional weekly **STUDY** notes...

WEEK TEN

dates: _____ to _____

...my study **GOALS** for this week...

This week's **READING** log:

DAY	BOOK	CHAPTER & VERSE

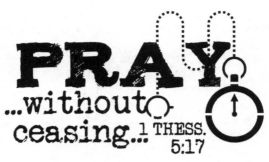

PRAY
...without ceasing... 1 THESS. 5:17

Give God **PRAISE** first:

_____

_____

_____

_____

_____

_____

_____

_____

_____

_____

_____

_____

Take your cares to the **LORD:**

_____

_____

_____

_____

_____

_____

_____

_____

_____

_____

_____

_____

...ponder...**WRITE**...doodle...**DRAW**...

Give thanks to
THE LORD
...He is good...
PSALM 136:1

I am
very, very
thankful for...

_____

_____

_____

_____

_____

_____

_____

_____

_____

_____

_____

_____

_____

...ponder... **WRITE**...doodle... **DRAW**...

...additional weekly notes of **THANKS**...

...all scripture is...
GOD-BREATHED
2 TIM. 3:16

Favorite **SCRIPTURES**:

THEMES & KEYWORDS:

...ponder...**WRITE**...doodle...**DRAW**...

...additional weekly **SCRIPTURE** notes...

_____
_____
_____
_____
_____
_____
_____
_____
_____
_____
_____

...my weekly Bible **MEMORY** verse...

_____
_____
_____
_____
_____
_____

How does this
week's study
**APPLY TO
MY LIFE?**

_____

_____

_____

_____

_____

_____

_____

Who can I **SHARE**
God's word with this week?

This week's **STUDY** notes:

...ponder...**WRITE**...doodle...**DRAW**...

...additional weekly **STUDY** notes...

WEEK ELEVEN

dates: _____ to _____

...my study **GOALS** for this week...

This week's **READING** log:

DAY	BOOK	CHAPTER & VERSE

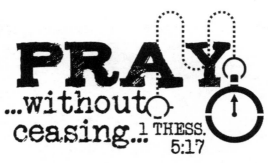

PRAY

...without ceasing... 1 THESS. 5:17

Give God **PRAISE** first:	Take your cares to the **LORD:**
_____	_____
_____	_____
_____	_____
_____	_____
_____	_____
_____	_____
_____	_____
_____	_____
_____	_____
_____	_____
_____	_____
_____	_____

...ponder...**WRITE**...doodle...**DRAW**...

Give thanks to
THE LORD
...He is good...
PSALM 136:1

I am
very, very
thankful for...

_____

_____

_____

_____

_____

_____

_____

_____

_____

_____

_____

_____

...ponder...**WRITE**...doodle...**DRAW**...

...additional weekly notes of **THANKS**...

...all scripture is...
GOD-BREATHED
2 TIM. 3:16

Favorite **SCRIPTURES**:

_____

_____

_____

_____

_____

_____

_____

_____

_____

_____

THEMES & KEYWORDS:

_____

_____

_____

_____

_____

_____

_____

_____

_____

_____

...ponder...**WRITE**...doodle...**DRAW**...

...additional weekly **SCRIPTURE** notes...

_____

_____

_____

_____

_____

_____

_____

_____

_____

_____

...my weekly Bible **MEMORY** verse...

_____

_____

_____

_____

_____

_____

How does this week's study APPLY TO MY LIFE?

_____

_____

_____

_____

_____

_____

_____

Who can I SHARE God's word with this week?

This week's **STUDY** notes:

...ponder...**WRITE**...doodle...**DRAW**...

...ponder...**WRITE**...doodle...**DRAW**...

...additional weekly **STUDY** notes...

WEEK TWELVE

dates: _____ to _____

...my study **GOALS** for this week...

This week's **READING** log:

DAY	BOOK	CHAPTER & VERSE

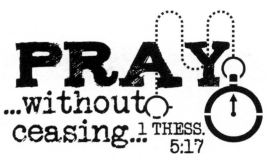

PRAY
...without ceasing... 1 THESS. 5:17

Give God **PRAISE** first:

_____
_____
_____
_____
_____
_____
_____
_____
_____
_____
_____
_____
_____

Take your cares to the **LORD:**

_____
_____
_____
_____
_____
_____
_____
_____
_____
_____
_____
_____

...ponder...**WRITE**...doodle...**DRAW**...

Give thanks to
THE LORD
...He is good...
PSALM 136:1

I am
very, very
thankful for...

_____

_____

_____

_____

_____

_____

_____

_____

_____

_____

_____

...ponder...**WRITE**...doodle...**DRAW**...

...additional weekly notes of **THANKS**...

...all scripture is...
GOD-BREATHED
2 TIM. 3:16

Favorite SCRIPTURES:

_____
_____
_____
_____
_____
_____
_____
_____
_____
_____

THEMES & KEYWORDS:

_____
_____
_____
_____
_____
_____
_____
_____
_____

...ponder... **WRITE**...doodle... **DRAW**...

...additional weekly **SCRIPTURE** notes...

_____

_____

_____

_____

_____

_____

_____

_____

_____

_____

...my weekly Bible **MEMORY** verse...

_____

_____

_____

_____

_____

_____

How does this
week's study
**APPLY TO
MY LIFE?**

_____

_____

_____

_____

_____

_____

Who can I **SHARE**
God's word with this week?

This week's **STUDY** notes:

...ponder...**WRITE**...doodle...**DRAW**...

...ponder... **WRITE**...doodle...**DRAW**...

...additional weekly **STUDY** notes...

...ponder...**WRITE**...doodle...**DRAW**...

PRAISE THE LORD!

...you finished it...

Don't stop your weekly
Bible study journey now.

Keep on **READING** it,
PONDERING it,
ABSORBING its message,
SHARING it with others,
& APPLYING it to
your daily **LIFE**.

Thank you for using one of our journals!

Our family appreciates your purchase and feedback. If you found this journal useful (hopefully a bit life-changing too), we ask you to tell a friend and consider writing a review. Our goal is to spread the good news of Jesus and inspire others to learn more about God's word...one journal at a time.

With much ♥,
The Frisby's
Stephen, Shalana & Rowynn

p.s. Check out our website for other fun journals!

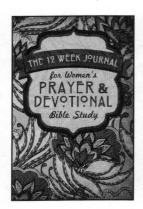 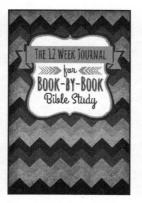 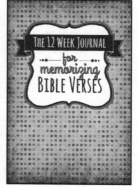

1.2.3... journal it!

find more about us at www.123journalit.com
... self-guided DIY study books for the whole family ...

If you like this journal, please share it and spread the word! #123journalit

Made in the USA
Columbia, SC
17 December 2017